THE MANY MOODS OF
BILL BAILEY ™
SONGS 1995 - 2005

All Music and Lyrics by   Bill Bailey
(except 'Leg of Time' co-written by Sean Lock)

© 2007 BBm Ltd.
℗ 2007 BBm Ltd.
First Edition 2007
ISBN 0978-0-9557412-0-3
ISMN M-9002143-0-0

Published by BBm Ltd.
18 Seafield Avenue
Edinburgh
EH6 7QG

www.billbailey.co.uk

Front Cover Art	Joe Magee
Song Transcription	Steven Markwick (Tim Pike)
Project Manager	Gillian Robertson
Design	21nine Advertising and Design
Printer	Scotprint

Thanks to   Roslyn Gaunt, Sam Oakley, Tony Briggs, Karen Koren and Pat at PBJ for all their help compiling the photos and tour posters.

Many thanks to   Gillian at BBm for guiding the project onwards to victory.

Special thanks to   Kris and Dad.

For Dax.

FOREWORD

At last! After so long spent merely listening to the bearded one's music, you can finally hold it in your own human hands. Amidst the pages of this book awaits a world of possibility, a world of racially harmonious zebras, insect slave-lords and winged beasts of the night that can be summoned up with a few chords. A monstrous body of work that has been tamed for your playing pleasure.

This may all seem a bit much if you've always thought of Bill Bailey as just a stand-up who occasionally sings.

Bill's music is capable of creating complex yet memorable compositions - intricate lyrical explorations of his uniquely absurd ideas. In Insect Nation, for example, he takes the simple premise of an insect ruled apocalypse and delights in examining every possible facet of it, even providing a back story which allows us to sympathise with our insect rulers. It is this dynamic, the vigour and sincerity with which he treats even the most whimsical of concepts, which makes him stand out in the field of musical comedy.

At times his music can even be poetic. Love Song's lyrics are tinged with a judicious excess that gives them just the right balance between humour and conviction. It's an example of his ability to playfully deconstruct the music that he creates, as in Insect Nation when he searches for his inner - insect high, low and behind the Pringles.

His songs can be equally as affectionate. Unisex Chip Shop is a warm-hearted tribute to Billy Bragg and the two played it together on stage after a chance meeting at the Glastonbury Festival.

But ultimately it is the strength of the song writing that makes his music so enduring. The catchy melodies and often surreal lyrics have gained these songs a cult following, and this book is an opportunity for you to spread the joy in whichever way you choose. So whether you'd like to strum Hats off to the Zebras round a camp fire, lull your children to sleep with Nemesis of the Vole, or perhaps serenade your (ex) lover with Love Song, be sure to do justice to the work that went into creating this music. And, if you have any, try adding some bongos. Or a gong.

Josh Cluderay

Rockin' out, live 'Part Troll' Hammersmith Apollo, 2004.

MANY MOODS INTRODUCTION

These songs have not appeared on a soundtrack of a popular film. They have not reached a wider audience through their usage on a mobile phone advert. Probably because they are about Insects taking over the world, Zebras being a living embodiment of racial harmony, and Owls. Owls and Voles. Daft songs, really.

In this collection I hope to give you a flavour of my own psyche... a glimpse into the complex workings of my mind, a ray of light in these dark and troubled times. But failing that, I'll settle for having a bit of a laugh while you sing them in the bath, around a small fire, or as an audition piece to baffled looks.

One of the greatest accolades I can remember was when I bumped into the late, great John Entwistle, the bass player of 'The Who', as he was coming out of a night club. He looked at me for a moment, then said " Insect Nation" before getting into a car.
Respect to The Ox.

Hope you enjoy

Bill Bailey

THE MANY MOODS OF

BILL BAILEY ™

SONGS 1995-2005

Leg of Time   2

Insect Nation   10

Midnight in Parliament Square   20

Hats off to the Zebras   24

Unisex Chip Shop   32

Love Song   38

Beautiful Ladies   48

Redneck Redemption   54

Death Metal Lullaby (Nemesis of the Vole)   60

Edinburgh Festival Poster 1996.

Leg of Time

This was borne out of a show called 'Rock' which I wrote and performed with Sean Lock. It was a pastiche of all the pompous prog-rock songs of the '70s. It had to have fantasy elements, mythical beasts, a swan, and a pretentious concept i.e. Time having a 'leg'. In the show, while I played the song, Sean would come on with a mannequin's leg which had a kitchen clock sellotaped to it, whilst dancing in the contemporary style. The relative cheapness of this prop was due to the fact that most of the budget had gone on a rock star style stretch trolley. Two shopping trolleys welded together, complete with smoked glass, leatherette handle, and headlights. This allowed my character the trappings of rock stardom, while still 'keeping it real' by going to the supermarket.

The Leg of Time

Bill Bailey & Sean Lock

Rock, straight 8s ♩ = 90

The jes-ter hops on the Leg of Time

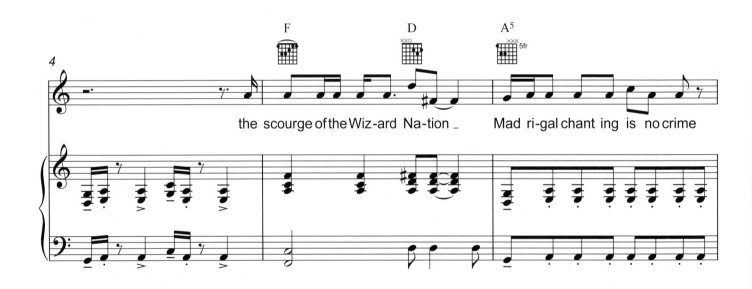

the scourge of the Wiz-ard Na-tion _ Mad ri-gal chant ing is no crime

when you're suc-kled by a blind Al-sa-tian - who stole the Leg of

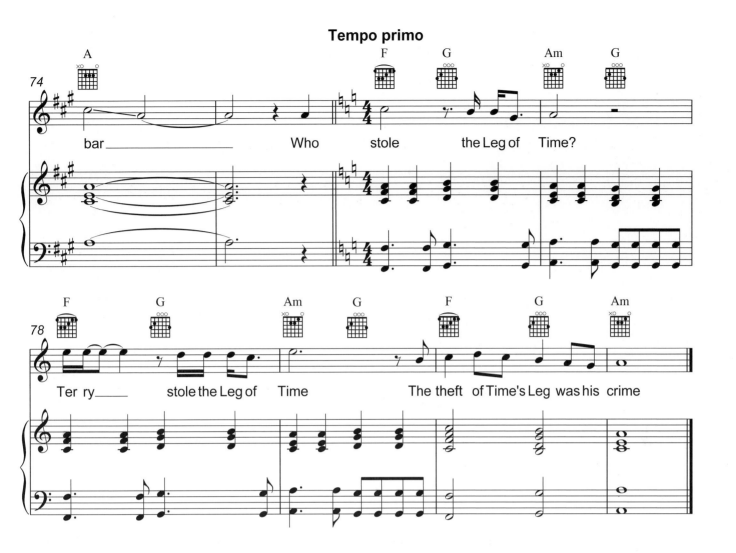

Tempo primo

bar_____ Who stole the Leg of Time?

Ter ry_____ stole the Leg of Time   The theft of Time's Leg was his crime

BILL BAILEY'S
cosmic jam

"FREQUENTLY HILARIOUS...
AND A DAMN GOOD
GUITARIST"
THE GUARDIAN

"DELIRIOUSLY FUNNY"
DAILY TELEGRAPH

SHOW STARTS
11:45 PM

11 - 2
AUG - SEP
NOT TUES 15,29

GILDED BALLOON
STUDIO THEATRE

VENUE 38

TICKETS £6/£5   BOX OFFICE:0131 226 2151

Edinburgh Festival Poster 1995.

9

Insect Nation

This was my attempt at a song dealing with dire apocalyptic warnings against damaging the planet. It's also based on the not unreasonable assumption that insects might take over the world, inspired by the knowledge that only cockroaches would survive an all out nuclear war. When I performed this on 'The Stand Up Show' for the BBC, Steve Coogan said to me 'it's very good that, this crazed paranoid character, you should work on that' and I nodded, but didn't tell him, that's me, that's what I actually think. Barry Cryer played the cymbals, and I had insect dancers which was quite a surreal experience.

Insect Nation

Bill Bailey

spid ers__ are not in-sects but in a war they will side with the in-sects trait-ors trait-ors spi-der trai-tors

they'll be-tray us and they'll make us hu man slaves in an in-sect na-tion Ah_____

hu-man slaves in an in-sect na-tion Ah_____ hu-man slaves in an in-sect

na-tion Ah_____ hu-man slaves in an in-sect na tion_

On stage with Pod during recording of Cosmic Jam, Bloomsbury Theatre 1996.

'Bewilderness'
Note the £2 coin as a plectrum, a nod to Brian May.

Midnight in Parliament Square

When Phil Collins sang 'Another day in Paradise' I knew there would be a homeless 'issue' song in the offing. This was a response to that, and when I perform it live, it invokes a cacophony of animal noises from the audience. Feel free to ad lib your own creatures that 'cry out in the night'.

Midnight in Parliament Square

Bill Bailey

How I imagine the cover would have looked if this had been a single in the '80's'.
Note sleeves rolled up, and the classic 'keyboard' tie. Great days.

Hats off to the Zebras

I wrote this as a tribute to Bryan Adams, it's to be sung in his style, and as a kind of 'Ebony and Ivory' homage. It's a plea for racial harmony through the medium of zebras, badgers etc. It is, I believe, the only instance where 'ring-tailed lemurs' appear as a song lyric, although I am quite prepared to be challenged on that.

Hats Off To The Zebras

Bill Bailey

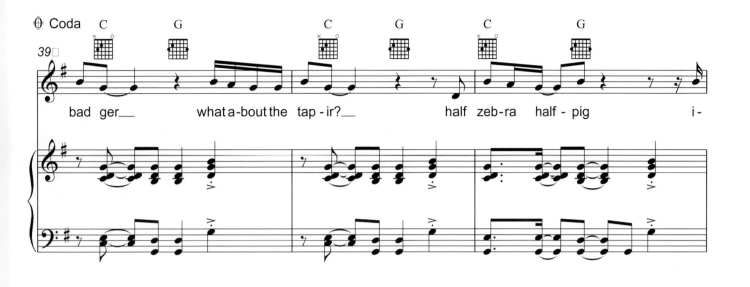

bad ger___ what a-bout the tap -ir?___ half zeb-ra half - pig i -

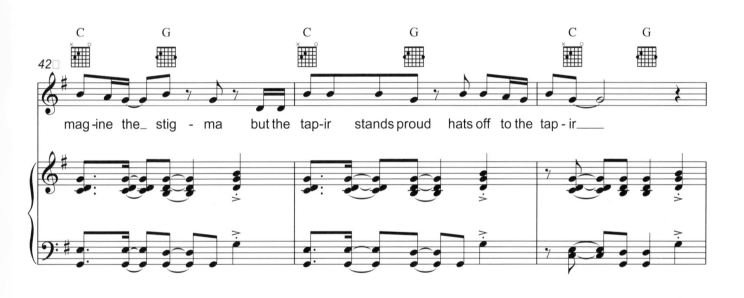

mag -ine the_ stig - ma but the tap-ir stands proud hats off to the tap - ir_____

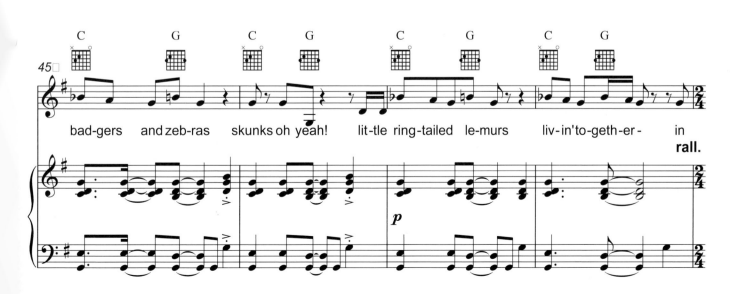

bad-gers and zeb-ras skunks oh yeah! lit-tle ring-tailed le-murs liv-in'to-geth-er- in

rall.

From an early moody, beardy shoot.

1998 Edinburgh Festival Poster. Note the classic 'hippy in flight' look.

Unisex Chip Shop

One of my favourite artists is Billy Bragg, and this is an affectionate tribute to his style. It should be sung in the Bragg idiom, and played ideally on an electric guitar at a festival somewhere. It's about sexual equality in the workplace. It's one of my favourites to perform, as I feel quite sorry for the character who can't stand up to the skinheads. I have written alternative endings where he despatches them ninja-style to win the respect of Debbie, but it's not the same.

Unisex Chip Shop

Bill Bailey

skin-head gang they snatched the fork from my hand   Debb ie _ she looked at me

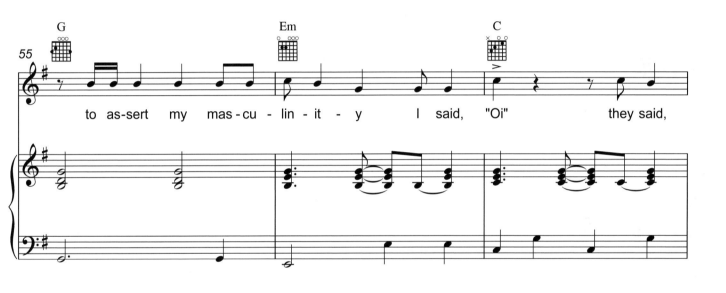

to as-sert my mas-cu-lin-it-y   I said, "Oi"   they said,

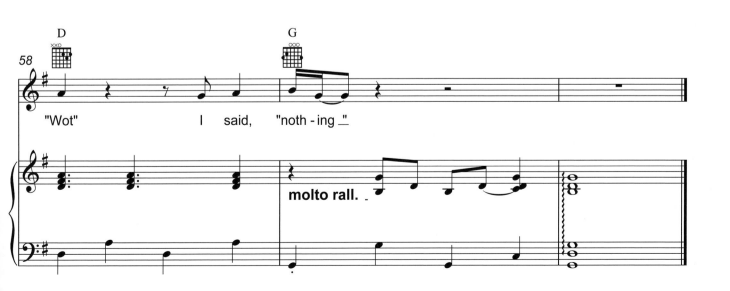

"Wot"   I said, "noth-ing _"

molto rall. _

ONE NIGHT ONLY!

PBJ & *GILDED BALLOON* PRODUCTIONS PRESENT

Bill Bailey

"He is an unalloyed pleasure, a treat for the funny bone, the brain and the ear" NEW YORK TIMES

USHER HALL 28 SEPTEMBER

SHOW STARTS: 8.30PM / TICKET PRICES: £14/£12.50/£9.50

USHER HALL LOTHIAN ROAD, EDINBURGH / BOX OFFICE: 0131 228 1155 / www.gildedballoon.co.uk

design @ thewinchestersuite.co.uk

Love Song

I discovered a terrific album called 'Scott Walker sings Jacques Brel' and loved the combination of his crooning style and the story-telling of the Belgian master. It was also a reaction to the blandness of so much pop. I like to think it's sung by the same character who tries to win Debbie in the chip shop, after he's been knocked back a few more times.

Love Song

Bill Bailey

things that I ___ had nev-er seen like a   snow-flake that melts   on the eye-lash of a start-led deer

Or ___   the paint ing of a dog _ that wears a

deer stalk-er and smokes a pipe that madeyou laugh so heart il -y   that I had pre-v'ous-ly thought   was

rub- bish _   Or the duck that lands so clums il -y on a

six-ty cig-ar-ettes a day   and   coughs a way his life   in the   cold ne-on re - search lab___   of your be-

trayal___   of your be - trayal_____

Not a bad look, the 'bowler', and the one massive hand.

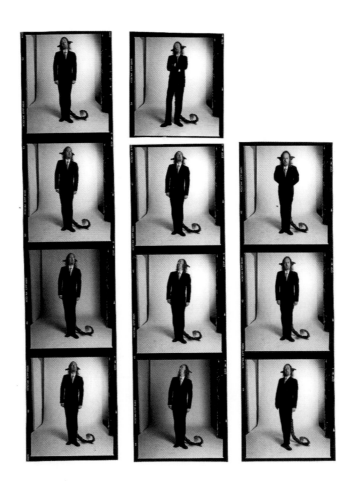

'Part Troll' Photo Shoot.

Beautiful Ladies

Ah, the wonder that is Chris de Burgh. This is his perfect moment. It was inspired by some half-remembered comment I heard him make about 'ladies' and how he might be the best person to propagate the human race, or something... Anyway, it contains one of my favourite lines, 'there shall be no clemency'.

Beautiful Ladies

Bill Bailey

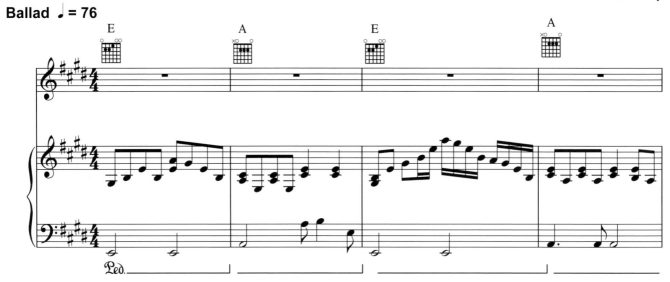

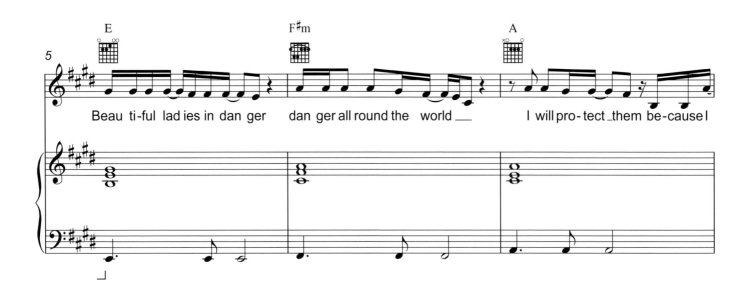

Beau ti-ful lad ies in dan ger   dan ger all round the world ___   I will pro-tect __ them be-cause I

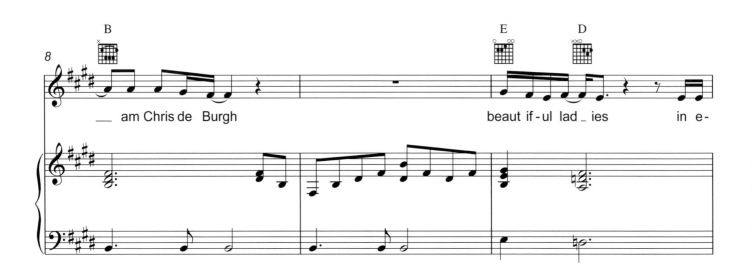

___ am Chris de Burgh   beaut if -ul lad __ ies   in e-

hide   and beau ty__   shall be my bride

Photo shoot for 'Bewilderness' in New York. This is 'Jakob',
our Triton Cockatoo, a rescue case we've had for some years.
There was a reason I was in 'Sergeant Pepper garb and in a library, but I've forgotten it.

Redneck Redemption

A song inspired by the extraordinary yet under-standable fact that America spends more on pornography than the combined debt of sub-Saharan Africa. It is written from the perspective of an ordinary Joe, a trucker lets say, who tries to help out with an act of self-sacrifice.

Redneck Redemption

Bill Bailey

Country swing ♩ = 164

Well I'll put my-self thru sex

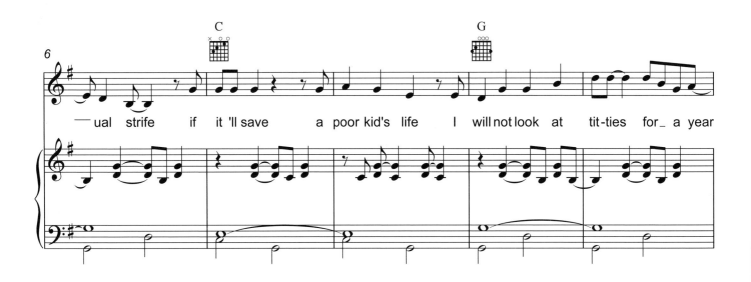

—ual strife if it 'll save a poor kid's life I will not look at tit-ties for_ a year

If it stops an I-raq-i be com ing dead I won't spill my seed_ on a

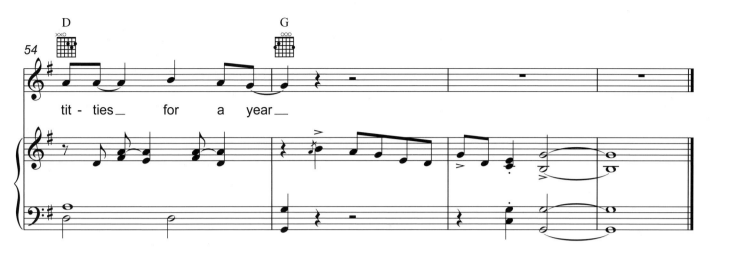

tit - ties __ for a year __

Edinburgh Festival Poster 1997.

Death Metal Lullaby
(Nemesis of the Vole)

I thought it would be fun to write a lullaby in an inappropriate style, and metal seemed the obvious choice. I had this vision of a hairy, leather-jacketed rocker dad singing to his child, with all the amps and guitars set up in the bedroom. (a vision which I have now fulfilled myself). And for the owl enthusiast, (for they are legion) the owl I had in mind was the Barn Owl. I am particularly proud of the line 'borne on the velvet wings of night', which, if you've ever seen a Barn Owl hunt, is a pretty accurate description.

Death Metal Lullaby (Nemesis of the Vole)

Bill Bailey

Rock, straight 8s $\quad \bullet = 158$

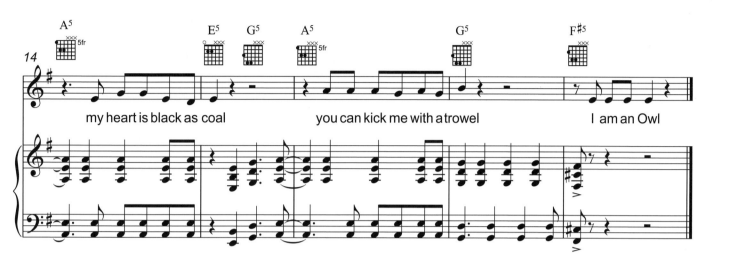

my heart is black as coal   you can kick me with a trowel   I am an Owl

o be continued...